Dedicated to my loving great grandfather Michael. Thank you for bestowing your wisdom on me and sharing the secrets of your garden.

My grandfather once explained to me why his bush of roses were so precious to him. There was a rose for Grandma Girly, Grandma Yasmin, Auntie Tika, my father, Lezlee, and one for me.

"When you love people," he said, "you must give them room to grow, weed out what can harm them, and feed them love; you will see them bloom into wonderful people."

The next morning, grandfather called for me to join him in the garden. Grandfather was going on a trip and gave me the task of watching over his garden. Grandfather whispered, "I want you to keep a careful eye on my rose bush. Water it, love it, and watch it grow." I listened carefully as my Grandfather entrusted me with his recipe of love.

The next day, I stood on the porch and wrapped my arms around grandfather. I leaned in close, smelling the aromas of ripe tomatoes, fresh cucumbers, and wild rose seed on his worn-down flannel shirt.

Cucumbers

Tomatoes

Seed

I watched as grandfather moseyed down the steps and carefully climbed into his beloved shiny deep-blue '81 Cadillac and swiftly drove down the road.

While Grandfather was gone, I struggled with the challenges of his garden. I tended his vegetables well, but a mistake landed me a piece of my family heritage...

On Monday, I saw one friendly crow that squawked hello as he swooped down into the garden and flew away with a rose. On Tuesday, I saw two wacky crows who wanted to play but not before swooping a rose away.

Monday

Tuesday

On Wednesday, I saw three silly crows who played with the water hose right before rolling a rose away. On Thursday, I watched four hungry crows pick at a rose as if it was a delicious buffet.

A little too much water and a hungry bird population damaged much of my grandfather's rose harvest.

On Friday, when Grandfather returned, he took a close look at his beloved rose bush. I was afraid that he would be upset with me. Instead, he split the bush to teach me a lesson on how to garden.

We began my own rose garden from the roots of my grandfather's bush. We transplanted the roots, and he taught me how to properly care for the roses to make them grow lush and beautiful.

In the early morning, he taught me about feeding the birds, something I had often seen him do but never questioned.

With Grandfather's guidance and recipe of love, I too grew my very own rose bush. The rose bushes have renewed themselves many times over. They are quite old, yet they still display beautiful blooms and a heavenly smell.

Over the seasons, I have learned that some of the tiniest seeds grow into the biggest flowers, adding beautiful color to the garden. In a person's life, a dream is like a tiny seed. If nurtured properly with attention, planning, and hard work, a dream can become a reality. I did not know it then, but I now know that by taking time with me, Grandfather cleared a space in his garden and shined his light on me.

My grandfather became my gardener, allowing me to bloom. I often reflect on the conversation my grandfather and I had.

We were working in his vegetable garden when he said, "Look here," pointing to the corn kernels and dried beans in my hand.

"That's just like Grandma Girly and me."

"Yes, sir," I replied, remembering my manners but wondering if maybe Grandfather had been in the garden sun too long that day.

Chuckling to himself and wiping the dirt on his pants, he continued, "I am like the corn stalk, straight and strong. I shelter Grandma Girly and my family from things that would hurt us."

I nodded my head, but I still did not know what he was talking about.

"She's like the bean," he laughed. "I make Grandma feel secure and safe, so she grows more in life, and she supports and helps me like the bean does growing its vine along the corn stalk. See, we help and care for each other just like the beans and the corn."

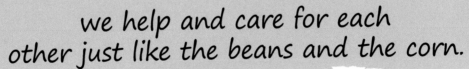

we help and care for each other just like the beans and the corn.

So, it went each April. I thought we were planting a garden, but Grandfather knew he was planting lessons in love and life. The best gift from my grandfather's garden, though, is the memory of a time when life was sweeter and slower, and people still stopped to share the harvest and even smell a rose or two.

April

I can still see him there in my mind. He is dressed in a buttoned-up flannel shirt and khaki work pants, with the richest dark chocolate skin tone that brings out his unique brown eyes circled in blue.

Grandfather was a simple man, small in stature but big and generous at heart. His garden reflected that. He planted in every nook and cranny he could. Vegetables and flowers thrived in every corner of the backyard.

If the family could not eat all the produce, it was given away to friends and neighbors.

I learned the value of hard work in that garden. I worked side by side with him more times than I can remember. Planting, weeding, and harvesting were all part of teaching me that every living thing has a love cycle. You must give it room to grow, weed out what can harm it, and feed it love; you will see it bloom into the most beautiful thing.

Grandfather's garden.
I can still see it in my mind.

Made in the USA
Monee, IL
20 June 2021